SIX AND SIX

Designed by Chestnut House/Dick Martin

Illustrated by

Ed Atchenson
K. Y. Craft
Pat Maloney
Andrew Epstein
Dezso Csanady
Dick Martin

**Structural
Reading Program**

SIX AND SIX

Toni Gould
Kathleen Teague

 RANDOM HOUSE School Division

Toni S. Gould is most grateful to Lynn McVeigh
for contributing her imaginative ideas and
creativity to some of the stories created in
this reader.

Contents

THE MIX-UP GAME

Kate and Bob ran to sit with Dad.

"Dad, play a game with us," said Kate.

"O.K.," said Dad. "What will it be?"

"The mix-up game," said Kate.

"That game is lots of fun," said Bob. "You can go first and then Kate can go. I will be last."

Dad sat back to think.
"I have it," he said.
"A man was in a rush. He
shut the bus and
ran for the gate."

"Ran for the gate,"
said Bob with a grin.
"You shut a gate and
run for a bus."

"No, Bob," said Kate.
"If you fix the mix-up,
then it is not fun."

"O.K.," said Bob.

"I am next," said Kate. "I made a list of things that I must do.

"I must dust the grass and rake the desk.

"Then brush the clock and set the dog."

"Bob, you go next,"
said Dad. "Did you think of
a mix-up.?"

"I have lots of them,"
said Bob.

"We skate in school and
spell on the lake.

"We wave a cake and
we bake a flag.

"Mom mends the beds
and makes the socks."

Mom came in to get
Bob and Kate for bed.

"This game is such fun,"
said Kate. "Can we go to
bed when we get up?"

"Go to bed when you
get up?" said Mom.

"It is a game we play," said Dad. "We mix things up."

"Mom, you think of one," said Kate. "Then we will go to bed."

"I think I have one,"
said Mom. "Time for school,
so off to bed!"

Thanks to Jane

"Tell me, Jane," said Mom. "How was the first day? Did you have fun?"

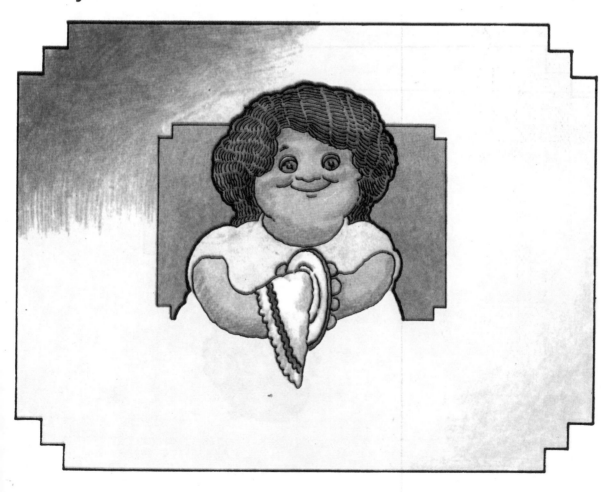

"No," sobs Jane. "I will not go back. The boys and girls went out to play tag. They did not ask me. I just sat at my desk."

The next day Jane did
not wish to go back. But
her mom made her go.

That day was as bad
as the first day.
And so was the next.

Jane just sat. She did not play with the boys and girls. They did not ask her.

Then one day it was Pet Day at school.

Jane had a chimp for a pet. Her mom let her take Chimp to school.

What a day for the boys
and girls! A chimp at school!

Chimp ran and sat at
Miss Lane's desk. He put
her hat on.

Jane went to get Chimp, but off he ran. What a chase!

All the boys and girls ran to help Jane.

With Ted's help, Jane got Chimp back in his box. The boys and girls had lots of fun with Chimp.

And thanks to Jane, it was the best Pet Day!

At the Lake

"It is so very hot,"
said Dad. "Hop in and we
will drive to the lake."

"Dad," said Bill, "can we take King with us? He looks hot, too."

"Hop in, King." said Dad with a smile.

Bill and King made a
dash for the lake.

Splash! Splash!
Bill and King were in
the lake.

"Look at that!" said Ann.
Bill and King made
waves in the lake.

Bill came out of the lake and went on the rides. He went on the swings and down the slide.

Bill met lots of boys and girls to play with. He did not miss King.

It was time to go.
Ann came to get Bill.

"Bill, get King and go
to the car," said Ann. "We
have to go. Mom said so."

"But King is with Mom
and Dad," said Bill.

"No, he is not," said Ann.
"I just left them and Dad
said he was with you."

"Help me look for him,"
said Bill.

"Tell me where to look," said Ann.

"The hot dog stand," said Bill. "I bet he went to beg for hot dogs."

"And there he is," said
Ann. "Just as you said."

"King, you are a bad
dog," said Bill. "You must
not beg for hot dogs. Go
back to the car."

On the ride back, King got up on Bill's lap.

"O.K., King," said Bill. "You are not a bad dog. You just like hot dogs."

HELP FOR MIKE

"Mike, I am late for my job," said Mom. "You must help me.

"I will give you a list of things to do."

Mike nods.

"Put the cups and plates in the sink," said Mom. "Put the milk away. Then go out and take in the trash cans. Take the socks off the line, but not if they are still wet.

"Then you can go out and play with the boys."

Mike put the cups and plates in the sink. He had so much to do.

He was sad.

"I will not make it," he said. "I will not make it in time for the races."

Just then the bell rang.

"It must be the boys," said Mike.

"Mike," said Bob, "look at the clock. We will be late and you have the stop watch. Mr. Crane said to bring it with us."

"I will get it for you,"
said Mike. "You can have it.
I can not go with you. I
have too much to do."

44

"But we can help you," said Ted. "What can I do?"

"Thanks, Ted," said Mike with a big smile. "Bring in the cans. Take my bike in, too."

"And me," said Bob. "I can help, too."

"Thanks," said Mike. "Put the milk away. Then help me take the socks off the line."

"We did it!" said Mike. "And we can still make the races. But we must run to get there in time."

As they ran Bob said,
"Mike, you can help me.
Run as fast as this, then
we will win all of the races."

48

And Mike did just that.
He came in first in not just
one race, but in all of them.

CAN IT BE?

Bob went for a ride
on his bike.

But he got a flat.

So he ran to get
his drum.

A drum can fix
a flat tire.

50

CAN IT BE?

Pam left her lunch box on her desk.

She ran back to get it.

But the lunch box was not there.

It ran to get in line for the bus.

Six and Six

"This is fun!" said Ted.

"I am next, Ted," said
Pam. "Let me ring the bell."

Jill and Peg got in line to get up on the truck. Next came Dan. But not Jeff. He ran to the back of the truck. He went to look in a big box.

"There is a dog in this box," said Jeff. "And she just had pups. I think there are six."

"Oh, no!" said the fireman. "What will we do with all those pups?"

"Let us have the pups," said Jeff.

"You can have the pups," said the fireman. "But you must bring a note from home. The note must tell us that you can have a pup."

The boys and girls ran home to get the notes.

In a flash Jeff was back.
He had his note.

"My mom said that I can
have a pup," said Jeff.

Jeff gave the fireman
his note.

Pam and Ted ran in
next. Then came Jill, Peg,
and Dan. They all had notes.

"This is it!" said the
fireman. "Six notes and six
pups."

58

The boys and girls ran to look in the box.

"You can not have the pups yet," said the fireman. "They are too little. I will tell you when."

The next day the girls
and boys came back to get
the pups.

But the fireman just said,
"Not yet!"

The fireman said the same thing the next day.

And the next day!

And the next day!

At last the fireman said,
"You can have the pups!"

What a Ride!
What a Place!

"I have a story to tell,"
said Jan.

"Go on," said Miss Peck.
"Tell us a story."

Jan got up to tell
her story.

"It is about a bus,"
said Jan. "A school bus like
the one we ride."

"Mr. Gates drives the bus. He picks up the kids, and takes them to school. After school he picks them up and brings them home.

"All the kids like Mr. Gates. He tells lots of jokes."

"One day, the boys and girls got on the bus to go to school. But when the bus got to school, it did not stop.

"Mr. Gates put the brakes on, but still it did not stop. The bus went past school."

"The bus went up the hill. Then it came down the hill. That was lots of fun.

"The bus went so fast that the boys fell down. And so did lots of girls!"

"At last the bus came to a stop.

"'What a ride!' said Mr. Gates.

"'What a place!' said the kids as they got off the bus."

"There was a long path with pines on one side of the path. The kids ran to look at the pine cones.

"But they were not cones. They were canes. Lots and lots of canes!

"What fun the kids had! Mr. Gates had a taste, too!"

"At the end of the path, there was a lake. Mr. Gates and the kids ran to the lake. Mr. Gates had a taste.

"'This is not a lake,' said Mr. Gates. 'It is a milkshake.

"What a day!'"

"Well, that is the end,"
said Jan with a grin.

Do you think a bus can
run off like that?

And do you think that
there is such a place?

PETE'S PALS

 Pete was a little boy who was very shy.

 Pete did not play with the boys on his block. He was too shy to ask them to let him play.

But Pete was not shy
with Miss Ross.

She ran a pet shop.
The pets in the shop were
Pete's pals.

Pete gave the cats milk.
Then he fed the fish. He
put a splint on a pup's leg.

"Pete," said Miss Ross.
"You are just like a vet."

One day Miss Ross said, "Pete, I have to go out. You take care of things. I left the milk for the cats on the shelf."

Miss Ross put on her hat, and went to get the bus.

Pete went to get the milk for the cats.

"I smell smoke," he said. "There must be a fire out in the back."

Pete ran to look in back
of the shop.

There were flames in the
trash cans.

Pete ran to the fire box.
He rang the fire bell. Then
he ran back and got the
pets out of the shop.

When Miss Ross got
back, the fire was out.

But the men were still
in the shop.

"The pets are safe,"
said one of the men.

"That boy got them
out just in time."

Miss Ross ran and gave
Pete a big kiss.

"Thanks to you," she
said. "The pets are safe."

The next day the story
about the fire was on T.V.
And so was Pete!

It was fun to be
on T.V.

Pete was not so shy
after that. He had lots to
tell the boys on his block.

84

Can You Tell?

Who tells jokes?

Mike or a bike?

Who sits up and begs?

A cup or a pup?

Who drives a crane?

A man or a can?

Who hides in a hole?

A pole or a mole?

Can You Tell?

What swings?

A gate or a plate?

What tells time?

A block or a clock?

What has cones?

A nine or a pine?

What has buds?

A nose or a rose?

Where is the Fire?

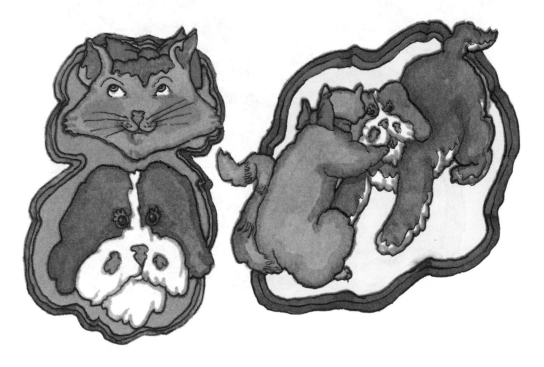

Jip is a dog and Muff is a cat. Jip likes to play with Muff. But Muff will not play with Jip.

Muff came out to sit in the sun.

So did Jip.

But he came to play with Muff.

But Muff ran and hid
from Jip. Muff ran into the
shed. Jip ran in after her.

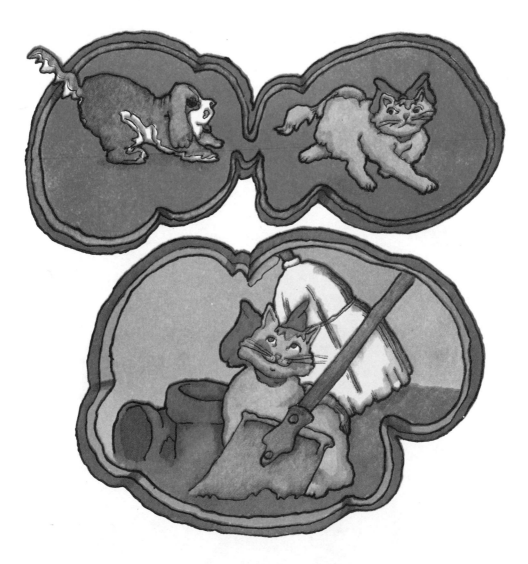

When Jip went in, Muff came out. She ran to the steps.

Jip came out of the shed. He went to look for Muff. When Jip got to the steps, Muff ran up the tree.

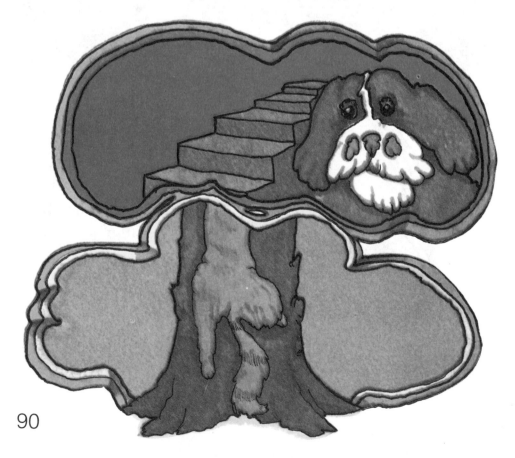

When Jip got to the tree, Muff was at the top.

Jip just sat by the tree. He sat and sat. So did Muff, but up in the top of the tree.

After a time, Jip got up and ran to look for a bone.

Eve came home from school. She ran past the tree.

"What was that?" she said.

"Is that Muff stuck up in the tree?"

Eve ran to get Mom.

"Mom," sobs Eve, "Muff is up in the tree. And she can not get down."

Mom gets a bench, but she can not get up to Muff. "Eve," said Mom, "get Dad and tell him to help us."

"Dad can not get to Muff," said Eve. "She is up at the top of the tree. What can we do?"

"I will get help," said Dad.

At last, help came. And
so did the boys and girls
on the block.

They came to see the
fire truck.

A man on the truck said,
"Where is the fire?"

"There is no fire,"
said Eve. "Just my cat up
in the tree!"